DUCKS AND GEESE AT HOME

by
Michael Roberts

GW00685374

Edited and Illustrated by
Sara Roadnight

Cover Photograph: Young stock with Michael Roberts.

ISBN 0 947870 09 1

Published by
Domestic Fowl Research
Kennerleigh
Crediton
Devon EX17 4RS

Contents

INTRODUCTION

It has given me enormous pleasure to see the growth in the number of people keeping and showing duck. From the early seventies to the present day, there have been spectacular changes and improvements, particularly in the miniature and Call ducks.

This book was written to help those new to keeping ducks and geese, and to answer the multitude of questions asked. This edition has needed updating, particularly the diseases and ailments section, as research and new drugs have come to the fore.

The descriptions of the breeds have been kept concise. The full descriptions of these will be found in the Poultry Club Standards Book, available from the British Waterfowl Association.

Michael Roberts
Sara Roadnight

Mallard (Anas platyrhynchos platyrhnchos)

WHICH BREED?

The notes on these breeds are brief, but serve as a guide to choosing a breed for a specific purpose.

DUCK

These can be divided into five sections:

1) egg laying
2) egg laying and meat
3) meat
4) exhibition
5) bantam, miniature & Call ducks

1. Egg Laying:

Khaki Campbell, White Campbell, Buff Orpington, Indian Runner, Dun and White, Welsh Harlequin.

Khaki Campbell: This breed has been developed and commercialised mainly by Kortlang & Kortlang Ltd. An excellent egg layer with production of 300 and over per annum.

White Campbell: There are not as many White Campbells as Khaki and their laying capacity is less. Cherry Valley has produced a medium sized white laying duck which is sometimes confused with the pure White Campbell.

Buff Orpington: A much under-rated and attractive duck with a good egg laying record. Difficulties have arisen when trying to find a utility strain as opposed to an exhibition strain.

Indian Runner: Sometimes known as Bali Penguin or Bali Soldier, they come in a wide variety of colours: black, white, chocolate, mallard colour, fawn and white, fawn, trout coloured and Cumberland blue. Although some of these could be classified as exhibition birds, the original purpose of the Indian Runner was as a layer. Their eggs are large for the size of bird.

Dun and White: Rarely seen, Campbell size duck with markings similar to the fawn and white runner. Good egg layer.

Welsh Harlequin: An attractive breed, good forager. Beware of birds purporting to be Welsh Harlequin as some of them have become muddled with Silver Appleyard. They are a colour sport from the Khaki Campbell, so the bills must be dark.

2. Egg laying and meat:

Silver Appleyard, Saxony, Magpie, Muscovy.

Silver Appleyard: An attractive breed, about 1/3 larger than the Welsh Harlequin with quite distinctive yellow bills in both sexes. Marvellous table birds. When buying either Silver Appleyards or Welsh Harlequins, do go to reputable breeders, armed with both specifications.

Saxony: An active but heavy table bird from Germany with most attractive markings.

Magpie: Smaller than most ducks in this section, nevertheless they grow well. Finding well marked Magpies is difficult.

Muscovy: Although sometimes known as a Barbary duck but not generally classified as a domestic duck, the Muscovy has been sufficiently domesticated to warrant inclusion in this section. They come in several colour variations - white, white and black, blue, chocolate and white. Some people consider the taste to be gamier than other ducks. They fly well, so will need wing-clipping.

3. Meat:

Although all domestic ducks are good to eat, only one breed is outstanding in speed of growth and size and that is the Pekin.

Pekin: Nearly everyone gets muddled with the Pekin and Aylesbury. The Pekin has a yellow bill with a box-shaped head. The Aylesbury has a pinky-white bill with an angular head and a deep keel underneath. Pekin ducks form the basis of all commercial meat ducks and they mature at 10-12 weeks. They should have a tinge of canary yellow in their plumage.

4. Exhibition

Rouen, Aylesbury, Crested, Cayuga, Blue Swedish. These ducks of course lay eggs and can be eaten, but their primary use is for exhibition.

Rouen: An old French breed, really just a huge domesticated mallard, which even goes into eclipse plumage in the summer. Very slow to develop and rather lazy.

Aylesbury: Usually confused with the Pekin (see above) this large-keeled old table duck is slow in developing, but has a beautiful shape.

Crested: Smaller than the previous two, there are now several colours of the Crested. The white variety is particularly stunning. Difficult to breed them with perfect crests.

Cayuga: This attractive greeny-black breed comes from America and is a colourful addition to a collection. Their eggs vary from cream to dark sooty green.

Blue Swedish: An eye-catching breed of a beautiful blue-grey colour with a white bib and 2 white primaries. A large, heavy breed, they lay quite well, but it is difficult to get the colouring correct.

5. Bantam, miniature and Call ducks:

Black East Indian, Silver Appleyard, Call ducks. These are birds which do well in confined spaces, but Call ducks particularly are very noisy. They were used to decoy wild ducks to ponds with their incessant high-pitched quaking. These three varieties normally need wing-clipping as they are small enough to fly well.

Black East Indian: A beautiful, neat breed with beetle-green black plumage.
Silver Appleyard: Exactly like its large counterpart in shape and colour, but in miniature form. They are sometimes not very fertile.
Call duck: Various colours - white, pied, mallard, apricot, silver and blue. Attractive, round shape but very noisy.

Khaki Campbell drake

GEESE
These can be divided into four sections:

     1) egg laying
     2) egg laying and meat
     3) minority breeds
     4) exhibition

1. Egg Laying:

Chinese: An very graceful goose which comes in two colours, white and grey (the progenitor being the Swan Goose). The noisiest of all the breeds of geese, they make very good guards. Prolific egg layers of a smallish egg. Although there is little merit in crossing the Chinese with other breeds of geese, they will do so readily.

2. Egg Laying and Meat:

Embden, Utility Toulouse.

Embden: The tallest of all domestic geese and always pure white. They can attain weights of over 30lbs.

Utility Toulouse: Another large goose which crosses well with the above. Grey in colour.

3. Minority breeds:

Brecon Buff, American Buff, Pomeranian, Buff Back, Pilgrim, Roman.

Brecon Buff: True Brecons are hard to find with their pink bills and pink legs. A docile breed.

American Buff: Similar to the Brecon Buff but with bright orange bill and legs, larger than the Brecon.

Pomeranian: Imported by the DFT from the USA in 1983, this goose has proved to be a good layer and grows well. Attractive saddle-back grey and white markings.

Buff Back: Like the Pomeranian in size and marking, but buff instead of grey.

Pilgrim: The true Pilgrim is hard to find as it is the only goose which is sex linked, producing white ganders and grey geese. There are some grey and white geese advertised as Pilgrims but these are not sex linked and are probably Toulouse/Embden crosses. Beware!

Roman: A small and neat goose, pure white, and excellent for limited space. Beware of small Embdens being passed off as Romans.

4. Exhibition:

Sebastopol, African, Giant Dewlap or Exhibition Toulouse.

Sebastopol: An attractive pure white breed with long curling feathers. Good stock is difficult to come by as the degree of curled feather is important.

African: A large, heavy goose with a particularly deep voice and quiet temperament.

Giant Dewlap or Exhibition Toulouse: A specialist breed, and at the expensive end of the market. They are so over-developed that they have difficulty in breeding naturally. They come in three colours grey, white and buff.

MARKETING DUCK AND GOOSE EGGS

Duck: There is always a ready market for duck eggs, which are unrivalled for cooking with. Have you ever tried adding one duck egg to scrambled eggs? It really improves the taste and colour. However, it would be prudent to check the following outlets before embarking on large scale duck keeping for egg production. Price: 10-20p higher than free range hens eggs.

1. Roadside sign
2. Local Chinese restaurant or take away. Most Chinese recipes are based on duck eggs.
3. Local Farm Shop
4. Local Health Food Shop

Duck eggs have a short shelf life as the shell is so porous, and they should not be kept more than 10 days.

Geese: Although some people like to eat goose eggs, the main market is with crafts people who use them for decorating; they use the clear eggs from the incubator for blowing and painting, or unhatched ones, whether clear or dead-in-shell, for cutting open and decorating 'á la Fabergé'. Price varies between 50p-£1.00. A small advertisement in your local newspaper should produce the desired response, or you could visit some of the myriad Craft Fairs where these things are displayed, and get to know the people there.

ARE DUCKS EGGS POISONOUS?

During World War II there was a scare that duck eggs were poisonous. The poison concerned was salmonella and the reason for the eggs carrying it then was that many ducks were kept in filthy conditions, on ponds which were virtually open sewers. Today, with our Water Boards and tighter control of effluents, the risk of salmonella is remote.

BREEDING

Ducks

Most ducks start to lay eggs in the early spring, the timing depending to a great extent on the weather. Commercial Khaki Campbells will lay at 22-24 weeks old.

Separate the various breeds two weeks before setting eggs, as domestic duck will readily cross. Even so, you may still be caught out by free-flying mallard drakes! If you only have space for a pair of duck, that is fine, but if you have space for more be careful there are not too many drakes. A good ratio is 1:3, with two drakes to 5 to 6 ducks in the heavier breeds such as Pekins and two drakes to 8 to 10 ducks in the lighter breeds such as Campbells. As ducks are gregarious birds there should be little squabbling. The introduction of a fresh drake or younger ducks will lead to some bullying until they reorganise the pecking order, and it is important to add more water and food troughs at this stage to avoid newcomers being crowded out. Over active drakes have been known to try and mate with other species, including hens.

Prior to laying during the colder months of winter your birds will require additional layers pellets. Bring the ratio up to 50% wheat and 50% pellets until early May and drop back to 80% wheat, 20% pellets. Khaki Campbells benefit from being on 60% wheat, 40% pellets through the summer months. Feed at the rate of 7oz per bird per day in bowls or troughs to avoid wastage and mess, and move these feeders and drinkers to fresh ground every few days. This avoids those unsightly and unhealthy muddy patches.

Ducks lay in the morning, usually before 9am, so if you can let them out after this you will ensure the eggs are in the house and therefore collectable. It is imperative to regularly replace the straw in duck houses for the birds' comfort and hygiene, and to avoid contaminated eggs. Ducks lose their laying efficiency after three years, so either replace a few every year or the lot after three years.

Geese

Geese start to lay in early February - most people reckon on the first egg on St. Valentines Day - but this of course depends on the weather. The preparation for breeding of geese starts long before this. Try to get the geese organised into breeding pairs/flocks in the autumn as the pair bond is stronger than with ducks and they need time to settle down. The best ratios with small numbers are 1:2 or 1:3 and in flocks 2 ganders to 8 to 10 geese.

When the grass begins to lose its goodness in October it is time to start on extra feeding. It is important to feed geese well through the winter and although some say a hard winter will benefit fertility, correct feeding is vital - fit not fat is what to aim for. 60% wheat and 40% pellets at a level of 9oz per bird per day is a general guide, assuming they have access to grass for most of the time. Drop back to pure wheat/barley in April/May when the grass is growing again.

Geese like to choose their own nest site but do help them by making a small house as per diagram; a few fir branches stuck in the ground in a circle, even a couple of wooden pallets in inverted V form will do, to give some protection from the elements and winged vermin and to make it more private. Construct this away from the perimeter fence so that the fox will not disturb the sitting goose. You can also provide fresh straw in the main house and let them nest there.

Nestbox for ducks. The size can be suited to the breed of duck. The wire porch is to deter winged predators.

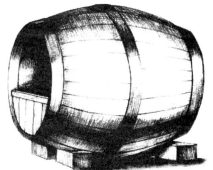

Houses suitable for laying geese

The first two eggs laid are normally infertile. Mark these with a waterproof felt pen and if you are going to let the goose sit, the marked eggs can be taken away when there are four or five in the nest. Geese normally lay every other day, and to ensure more are laid in the same place, leave two eggs in the nest, the last egg laid being the cleanest. This helps to extend the laying period. When she decides to sit she will pluck her down to line the nest. At this stage it is best to put back 2 or 3 stored eggs into the nest so that she has the possibility of hatching five goslings.

Problems arise when there are two geese and they want to sit on the same nest. If you allow birds to do this the normal result is no goslings at all as the eggs can easily get chilled while the geese are squabbling over who should have them. To avoid this, place a low partition of plywood between the two geese about 18cm high and well fixed. Leave two eggs in both nests so that they have a nest each and can still talk to and see each other. Normally one goose is more determined than the other so she will start to sit first. This may create problems at hatching time - one lot of eggs hatch and the other goose gets so over-excited and jealous that she may get up off her not-quite-hatched eggs and abandon them in favour of the new goslings. It is quite a good idea to have a few broodies available (although they never seem to be broody when you need them!) or the incubator turned on. If they are within 48 hours of hatching, or pipping you may still be able to get away with putting them in a warm place until they hatch. You will have to spray the eggs with tepid water when they start to hatch in this rescue operation, otherwise the membrane inside will dry out and become too tough for the gosling to break through. The natural moisture of the goose in the nest takes care of this under normal conditions.

You may find that young geese become too zealous and will not come of the nest to feed or drink. You will be able to test if this is the case by putting a bowl of food and water where only she can get at it. You will then have to chase her off, covering the eggs with down so that they are concealed. Geese seldom settle to incubation in their first year, but make better parents from their second year on. Depending on the size of the bird, a goose can sit on as many as twelve eggs, but it is better to restrict them to 6 or 8. If there are too many, the eggs on the outside can become chilled, so they will all get chilled in rotation as the goose turns them round.

Once the goslings are off, try to keep this area as quiet as possible: it can take up to 36 hours for them to emerge from the nest after hatching. The temptation to keep checking on progress is strong, particularly for children. Place a pan of chick crumbs nearby and gently drive the goose and her brood to it. The gander will be at his most protective, so stand up to him and talk or whistle to him. After a few days you will find goslings waiting for their additional food and this wants to be continued until they are really more interested in grass than anything else. Some goslings will not look at additional food if the parent birds do not eat it or if the grass is sufficiently nutritious, but this happens only occasionally. It is all too easy to starve goslings, assuming the grass is enough for them, so it is better to provide extra. They must have fresh water ideally twice a day in troughs 5cm high. Try to avoid large water containers for fear of drowning the goslings or chilling them through being too wet.

Deformities

Any bird that has an obvious deformity such as a bent spine, an improperly formed beak or blindness must be culled, or rejected if you are buying birds.

The Swan Goose
(Anser cygnoides)
above *is the progenitor of the*
Chinese goose
right

METHODS OF KEEPING

There are various methods of keeping ducks and geese. Included here are three methods for duck, the last two being applicable to geese as well.

Method A

Confined Area (duck only)

Do remember that domestic duck and geese are very destructive, so using the lily pond is out if you want to avoid a muddy mess with no lilies and no fish. To keep ducks successfully in a confined area calls for some planning, see diagram.

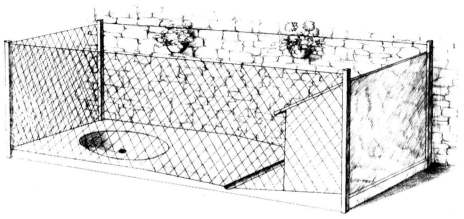

A design for a small duck enclosure.
Note the drainage system.

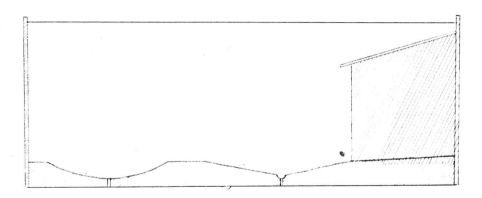

It is necessary that the drainage is well thought out and there is a readily available water supply which does not freeze in the winter. As your duck pen may be in an urban area, all-round fencing is needed against stray cats, foxes, dogs etc. Note that all the surfaces are sloping to one or several drainage points. All surfaces should be made of a strong mix of concrete, including the pond which should be regularly swilled down with water and cleaned out about every 2 days - the thumb over the end of a hose pipe to increase the pressure is ideal. The concrete base does not preclude you from enhancing the area with hanging flower pots out of the reach of the ducks. A luxury would be a small wooden plank so the ducks could stand on it for preening - warmer than concrete. The house can be a simple wooden construction with a step of 8cm on the lintel to stop litter from spreading into the run area. The best litter is shavings, then wheat straw.

Feeding is best in a shallow plastic basin with 70% wheat/barley, 30% layers pellets, and vegetable matter from time to time. Remember that as your birds are confined they have no access to natural foods, so save them some tasty snacks such as worms from the garden, brown bread, plain biscuits, mashed potato, plus most cooked vegetables chopped up. Raw vegetables are unpalatable and will merely rot. Soaked dog rusks or biscuits are popular. Always put any food in a plastic basin so there is less mess to clear up; you can see at a glance whether they like it or not, and it helps to keep the run clean and sweet smelling. If you leave food about you are attracting rats, sparrows and starlings, to say nothing of greedy cats.

Feed once in the morning and in the afternoon about 3-5pm depending on whether it is summer or winter. Remove the feeding basin after each feed, and if there is some left, feed less next time.

If you can let the ducks out into the garden for a certain time, even if only at weekends, they will benefit, but remember they are poor gardeners. They like slugs however, so early morning is the best time to catch these.

Numbers in this method: minimum two, maximum four birds.

Method B

Restricted area and limited free range (ducks and geese)

Some people will find they have an old orchard or area at the end of their garden which is suitable for ducks and geese: let us say an area of 20 metres x 30 metres. This is large enough for a pair of geese and up to 14 duck. The temptation is to have more, but the golden rule is to understock your land rather than overstock, even when the grass is growing really fast, otherwise you will have an unsightly and unhygienic mud bath.

If you find the run becomes muddy, not from overcrowding but from poor drainage, then an area of hard standing must be constructed. This area is made of concrete with a pond incorporated, and must be fox-proofed so that the birds can have free access at night or can be locked in on wet days or when you are away.

Before this area of hard standing is constructed, the drainage must be sorted out so that the pond can be cleaned (about every 2 days) and the concrete swilled down with water - you don't want the neighbours complaining of the smell. A netting roof can be added to keep cats, foxes and magpies from entering at will.

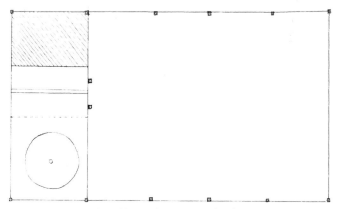

Plan of house, drainage, pond and run

The outside run can be constructed as follows: fencing of 1.83m x 5cm wire mesh pegged to the ground and supported by 5-8cm diameter tanalised 2.44m posts dug or knocked into the ground every 3 metres, with a tight line of plain wire on the top. This is effective against foxes when used with electric fencing (see Electric Fencing page no. 44). Additional water troughs in the run are advisable, particularly if ducks and geese are mixed, as geese will tend to hog the only one. Geese will not eat old or long grass, so it is better to tidy up the area, making sure there are no loose metal objects or bits of plastic string. Any trees or shrubs you wish to retain must be fenced with 1cm mesh to a height of 1.22m.

Method C

Unrestricted Free Range (ducks and geese)

This presupposes that you find yourself with a natural pond, stream, river, canal or lake. Every location is different but if it is impractical to fence off your birds, then you must have a holding area where they can sleep at night, where you can catch them or where they can lay eggs etc, preferably above the known highest flood line. Islands for safety are a myth - when ice appears the fox merely walks to catch his prey. Foxes can also swim well if the temptation is sufficient.

Ducks have a habit of laying in the water if they are let out too early (before 9am) as they habitually lay early in the day. Choose an area as large as you can which will include a house and feeding and water troughs, so the birds can be completely safe at night and safe if you have to be away.

Canals and some river banks will not always have easy access for the birds to be able to get in and out of the water, so you will have to either give them a ramp or dig away part of the bank.

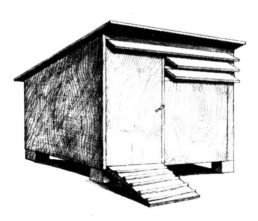

A free range duck or goose house

Fencing of sheep or pig wire is adequate for geese (duck will walk through it) but no deterrent to the fox (see Vermin page no. 44). For fencing across a stream use galvanised chain link down to the bed of the stream. This is bound to collect debris so will therefore need periodic cleaning.

Ducks and geese have to be taught where "home" is. When first establishing your birds, keep them penned up in the holding area for at least 2 weeks so that they learn their new surroundings, where and when they are fed and where they are housed. It takes ducks and geese a while to learn a new habit - they are naturally cautious - but once learnt, the habit sticks. You have to drive them into the house at night for the time they are confined. Then if possible fence in a small section of the pond or lake for a further week and get them used to going on the water and coming off in the evening. (If no natural water is available, the DFT has developed two sizes of self filling fibre-glass duck and goose ponds. These can be attached to the hose and moved from one place to another). Once it gets dark ducks will NOT get off the water but merely panic at your efforts which will cause both them and you unnecessary stress: so if they haven't got off the water by an hour before sundown you must drive them off. If the area of water is large, a rope held between two people and dragged across the surface is effective. However, if there are trees and bushes along the edges of the water, you will see the need to fence a small area so that you can drive the birds off easily. Teaching them in this way will save you much time and trouble late on, and help prevent your birds from becoming fox fodder.

If it is possible to fox-proof fence the entire area, water included, then you have an ideal situation. To prevent the water freezing in the winter, a small submersible pump such as is used in ornamental lily ponds and fountains will keep the water clear of ice. Beware also of rats (see Vermin page 46).

Running several different breeds of ducks and geese together will result in crossbreeding. The resultant progeny will cost as much to feed as pure breeds and will have no breeding value. In order to keep the breeds pure, you will have to pen them separately for about 2 months, or as long as you want to hatch the eggs. It takes about 10 days for semen from indiscriminate mating to become inactive, so wait a fortnight before setting eggs from the newly penned pure breeds. Free flying mallard will always be a problem as they readily mate with domestic duck. This is usually only discovered when you produce some curious crosses from pure birds - a telltale sign can be a new white ring around the neck.

Collection and Storage of eggs

It is important to collect eggs as early in the day as possible in order to prevent vermin getting them and to minimise frost damage. Both ducks and geese tend to lay early in the morning. When frost is still a danger, leave crock eggs in the nest to encourage the birds to lay in the same place next time, preferably in the house or a covered area; the covered area will confuse the winged vermin for a few weeks, but magpies in particular will look into, and enter housing in order to steal eggs.

When collecting eggs, mark each one with a waterproof felt pen or pencil and the date, breed and pen number, and keep records. In this way you will see who produced what and when, and this will save time in a breeding programme as it will be easier to discover infertile birds. If soiled, wash the eggs immediately after collection in water warmer than the eggs, or a solution of Virkon made by Antec. Reject any cracked, misshapen or unusual size eggs.

Store eggs in a cool, draught-free place in clean egg trays or on dry sand. They must be turned daily in order to keep the membrane moist, so mark one side and turn to the right one day and to the left the next, otherwise you will be winding the yolk up like a spring on the two thin "strings" (chalazae) which keep the yolk stable. Hatchability of stored eggs declines rapidly after seven days as waterfowl shells are very porous, so try and set them as fresh as possible. They need to be 24 hours old to enable the air sac to form to the correct size for the best oxygen supply.

Greylag (Anser anser) **left**, *the eastern race of which is the progenitor of most breeds of domestic geese including the Pomeranian* **right**.

16

HATCHING

1. Under Broodies

This is the traditional way and often gives the best results, as long as you have enough hens broody at the right time.

Broody boxes are best constructed as per the diagram and with wire netting on the base to prevent rats from burrowing in to the nest. The boxes are best set directly onto the earth which allows beneficial natural moisture to come up through the nest. They can be made in banks of any numbers, but four or five makes for easy handling before and after the hatching season. The boxes should be set in the shade on a small mound, about two turves high, in case there is a lot of rain. They must not get too hot as this is likely to put the broody off. Punch a shallow dip like a saucer in a turf and lay this, grass side down, in the box. Line the depression thinly with straw. Make sure the turf fits well so that no eggs can get rolled out into the cold. Put crock eggs or marked fresh eggs into the nest ready for the broody; she needs to sit steady on these for a few days before you put in the eggs you want her to hatch.

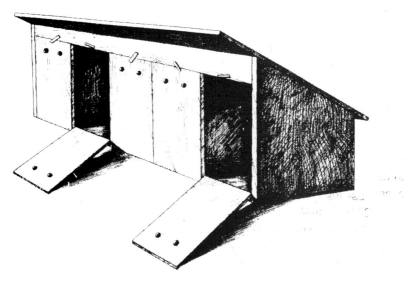

A bank of broody boxes

Select your broody from as large a breed as possible such as Sussex, Cochin, Orpington, Rhode Island Red, as using Silkies or Silkie crosses will limit the number of eggs you can set due to their small size. Although some Hybrid hens have been known to sit well, they are on the whole totally unreliable. Broodies will not want to leave their nest if they are serious, and will guard any eggs jealously, fluffing up their feathers and grumbling at you, even pecking at intruding hands. In order to check that your selected broody is serious, take any eggs out and slide your hand under her, palm up. She should "cuddle" your hand with her wings. You must delouse any broody with louse powder before getting her to sit for you as she will otherwise be irritated and disturbed by fleas. If your broodies are not used to being handled it is best to put them in a cardboard box with straw and eggs and close the lid. You will then be able to transport them to the broody boxes easily. Let them sit in the cardboard box to regain their composure for an hour or two and then you can pop them quickly into the broody box onto the crock eggs already there. Alternatively move them when it is nearly dark.

You will probably have to get your broodies off the nest every day. Try to do this at the same time, and tether them far enough apart so they cannot fight. To tether use a thong or piece of string attached to the broody's leg with a sliding loop and on the other end a curtain ring dropped over a metre high stick. Water and whole wheat only must be within reach, and the birds should be off the nest for about 20 minutes. Check that each one has defected before you gently put her back. If not, you may have to help this procedure by raising the hen to waist height and dropping her on the ground. Several times may be necessary. As you are putting her back on the nest check that her feet are clean - hen manure will easily turn the eggs bad. If you want to use the system they have at Slimbridge of putting broodies in individual wire cages when taken off the nest, it is an alternative to tethering them but involves more equipment.

Allow the broodies to sit on the crock eggs for a few days and get accustomed to whatever method you use for getting them off the nest each day. When they are used to the routine, it is time to set the eggs you want hatched. Try not to set duck and goose eggs together because of the difference in size. A large hen will take 11-12 duck eggs or 6 goose eggs, but if in doubt give her fewer. Put the eggs under her in the evening - remember to take out the crock eggs - and after about an hour check that she is covering them all properly. Take away any which are not covered.

A good broody will stay broody until she hatches off some youngsters. This may be after 28 days for duck eggs or three months if you are juggling the eggs around to make best use of the broodies. Don't be afraid of keeping a broody sitting on crock eggs until you are ready to set some hatching eggs, and then try to set two or three clutches where you have discarded infertile or bad eggs and you can start one of the broodies off on another clutch. If a broody becomes fierce and insists on pecking you she is only trying to protect her eggs. Offer your hand with your palm uppermost where the thicker skin will withstand the pecks better; turn your hand over once it is under the bird. Long sleeves are useful. Protective gloves are not really recommended as you can't feel what you are doing.

2. Under Ducks

Unlike geese, ducks which sit well make poor mothers. Most breeds of duck will go broody and Call ducks are sometimes used for hatching ornamental wildfowl eggs. Domestic ducks will hatch eggs but normally loose all sense of motherhood once the ducklings emerge. Muscovy ducks are the exception and make very good mothers, often hatching and rearing sixteen young.

Muscovy (Cairina moschata) drake

You can encourage a duck to sit on eggs by leaving them in the nest, or she may find a secret place to lay. She will then start to line the nest with down feathers so that when she comes off to feed and drink the eggs are left concealed.Also the warmth from her breast will transfer itself to the eggs much better when she has plucked out her feathers. Do not attempt to move her as she is most likely to desert. Try to encourage nesting in a safe area, preferably in the duck house. There may be times, if the duck sits too zealously, when you will need to drive her off the nest to feed. If you have to, do cover the eggs with the down which will conceal them effectively from prying eyes. It is often better to let ducks get on with incubating on their own as they can easily be disturbed and desert the nest.

Once the ducklings have hatched and are dry, fluffy and strong, they can be moved to a rearer coop and run.

3. Incubators

(Incubation: 28 days for duck, 28-30 days for geese)

If you have an incubator or can borrow one it is important that the manufacturer's instructions are followed closely. Incubation is a complete science on its own, everyone achieving different levels of success with seemingly identical equipment. Recommended reading is my book "Incubation at Home". It is important to stress that an incubator is only as good as the person operating it. Some breeders start duck and goose eggs under broodies and finish them in an incubator.

The main advantage of incubators over broodies is that they are available at any time of the year and they don't need feeding while they are not incubating.

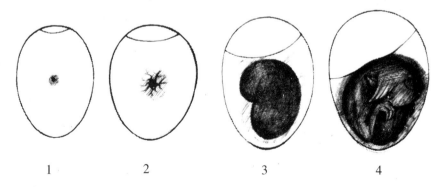

1   2   3   4

Stages in incubation: 1: 3 days, 2: 7 days, 3: 18 days, 4: 26 days.
(28 day period)

REARING

(ducks and geese)

1. Natural with Duck and Hen

Once the youngsters are dry and strong enough they should be moved from the broody box to the rearing coop and run.

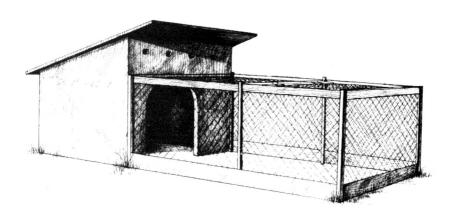

Place the coop and run as close to your house as possible, on the lawn, and try to keep dogs and cats away. The coop should have a solid floor with straw on it. The run must be covered on the top with wire netting to prevent predation by crows and magpies, as well as on the sides and base to stop rats burrowing in. If it is rainy, drawing-pin some heavy gauge polythene on the top and the side of the prevailing wind. The broody and the ducklings and goslings will move freely between the coop and the run, but to begin with put the food and water close to the coop end. Remember that your broody is now extremely hungry and thirsty. The first thing she will do when you put her in the run is to make a huge mess. Remove this, and give her some chick crumbs in a shallow pan. She will automatically call the youngsters to the food, and show them the drinker. It is still a good idea to dip the beak of each duckling or gosling in the water to get them started. The youngsters may not be hungry for the first day if the yolk sac has not been fully absorbed. The water must be in a drinker or font and never in an open dish otherwise the young will get chilled and may drown themselves. They must only have access to enough water at a time to drink and not to paddle or wash in until they are five weeks old or more. You may have to have two chick drinkers as they get older.

Two types of chick drinker

At about 10 days you will notice how anxious goslings in particular get for fresh grass. The coop and run must be moved regularly in any case to avoid yellow patches and mud holes. Make certain the front is on the coop at night and all the young are with the mother. At five to six weeks old you will notice that the youngsters are becoming more independent of their mother and are growing warm feathers, starting with the underneath. At this stage the hen can be taken away. Leave the Muscovy with her young, however, as she can take them out to free range.

The goslings will want room to graze and the ducklings will want more room to search for worms and slugs. Remove the run, and replace it with 61 - 92 x 5cm mesh chicken wire secured upright with bamboo canes (smaller wire for bantam ducks). Keep the run on short grass and enlarge it or move it around, always ensuring that the grass never becomes fouled. As your ducks and geese have grown, so your coop will have become too small. A shelter or house is needed in which they can be secured at night.

At this stage the ducklings and goslings can have a drinking trough. Both ducks and geese need to be able to immerse their heads in water to clean their tear ducts. The trough must be swilled out and filled with clean water every day - you will be surprised just how much mud and soil gets into it. Goslings may be given the trough earlier if the weather is kind. The area that the birds are now in, should be in partial shade as it is without the benefit of shade from the small run. The youngsters are particularly vulnerable to sunstroke until their back feathers have grown (see Ailments page no. 52).

Feeding: Ad lib chick crumbs for two weeks, growers pellets for 8 weeks, with wheat and grit from 4 weeks.

2. Artificial with Heat Lamps

Once your ducklings or goslings have dried out in the hatcher section of your incubator they can be placed inside a ring of exterior grade hardboard, in a stable, shed, garage etc. as long as it is draught and rat-proof. Buy 2 strips of hardboard 2 or 2.5m x 46cm and make a circle with them fastening with bulldog clips at the top and a brick on the floor. Fill the inside up to about 5cm deep with clean shavings. Put the chick crumbs in a shallow straight-sided dish like a flan tin. The young must have a font or water drinker and not an open bowl - they will either get chilled in an open bowl and develop pneumonia, or they will drown in it. Dip the beak of each bird in the water. Place the water font at the lowest edge of the circle so that the litter does not get too wet. For the heat use a ceramic infra-red lamp suspended from a beam or broom stick so that the heat is in the centre of the circle or to the side away from the water. The distance above the birds should be from 10 - 13cm. They will tell you if the lamp is at the wrong height by huddling together if too cold or by spreading out to the edges of the circle if too hot. Once you have found a starting level you should raise the lamp weekly, and in this way you will harden the birds off gradually. You may need several lamps depending on the number of birds, but normally 25 ducklings per lamp is enough (or 12-15 goslings). If they are drinking water very quickly, you may have to add more fonts.

You will soon notice that whereas during the first two weeks the birds need cleaning periodically, after the second week they will need cleaning out every day. The litter must be kept as dry as possible even though the birds do everything in their power to make it wet. Damp litter will lead to birds looking dishevelled and having chalky droppings. It is a good idea to put them onto small wire mesh at this stage.

After a week introduce some greenstuffs, particularly for the goslings: include lettuce, goose grass or cleavers and turves and renew daily. Geese have the instinct to pull grass from the day they are born and will rag ducklings or their fellow goslings unless they have access to grass. Ducklings and goslings can be reared together, but if possible try to separate them after two weeks to prevent ducklings being bullied. If pecking of wing feathers occurs and causes bleeding, spray with a gentian violet antiseptic spray which will prevent disease and disguise the red colour which is most attractive to the youngsters (hence the red base of most plastic water fonts).

The heat lamps can be turned off at three weeks, depending on the weather, and certainly during the day.

Get goslings out onto grass as soon as possible, but at least by six weeks, providing them with shelter as they can be silly in rainstorms. If the area is fox-proofed they will need the minimum of housing, otherwise they will have to be secured at night. Shady areas are essential.

Ducks and geese given access to swimming water after 6 weeks will feather up more rapidly than those with just drinking water.

Feeding: Ad lib chick crumbs for two weeks, growers pellets for 8 weeks with wheat and grit from 4 weeks.

*The mallard (Anas platyrhynchos platyrhynchos) **left** is the progenitor of all domestic duck including the Crested duck **right**, with the exception of the Muscovy.*

GENERAL MANAGEMENT

1. Handling

(a) Ducks and geese: hold the bird with legs between your fingers and the belly resting on the palm of your hand. In both birds the neck and head can be placed under your arm so the hissing and biting end is behind you. Hold the rear of the bird away from you as when birds are stressed by handling they make a mess.

(b) Ducks and geese: if the bird is very active hold it across the wings, the other hand supporting the bird under the belly if you have to carry it far.

(c) Duck only: Hold by the base of the neck. To be used for a short length of time only, such as from pen to a box.

Never throw a bird down after handling it, always put it down slowly talking to it and letting it go gently. The more the birds are handled the tamer they become as they realise you are not going to hurt them or be rough with them.

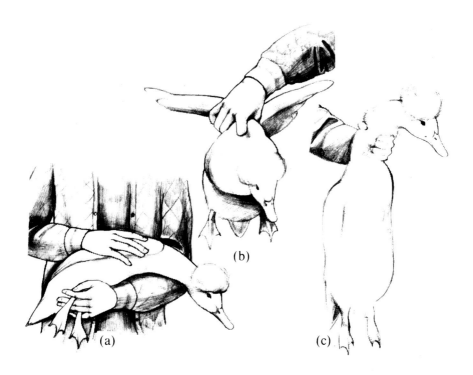

(b)

(a)

(c)

2. Catching

Free range ducks and geese are difficult to catch and they seem to know when you want to catch them. If there is a pond or large area of water, feed them away from this or drive them off as in the early training into the night holding pen. Once inside the pen a strong fishing landing net with a long handle is ideal and causes the least stress both to bird and catcher. Alternatively catch them in their house. If they have no permanent house and are within a complete fox-proof fence, try and corner them against the fence, again using the landing net; when you are trying to catch a goose or a gander and you have not got your landing net it will be hissing at you. Drive the bird into a corner which should make it face you. Move forward quickly and grab the bird by the neck. Beware of the wings which are powerful and will beat at your legs and shins.

Hold the bird firmly away from you, slightly squeezing the neck which will make it sit down. Move in quickly still holding it by the neck and pick it up. Try not to let the gander know you are frightened. Most of his act is bravado, so you must retaliate with same.

3. Gardens

Just a word of warning about letting your birds free range in gardens, woods or fields, old and new. There are certain poisonous plants such as Lords and Ladies, Ragwort, Foxgloves, Yew, Fools Parsley, Kingcup, and Hemlock which adult stock normally will not touch because they are bitter, but goslings might investigate out of curiosity. Geese will play havoc with trees and shrubs and will de-bark and de-foliate them. All young trees and shrubs will need well anchored protection in the form of 12mm wire mesh up to 1.2m high. Ducks will eat or trample on anything green.

4. Sexing Geese

This is a little bit of an art and practice makes perfect. Do not, however, practice on the same bird each time as you may damage it. Hold the bird as per illustration and gently squeeze on its back. By gentle and careful fingering towards the side of the vent, it can be opened. Sometimes, if the bird is relaxed, in the case of a gander the penis will pop out: other times it will tuck it away and gentle massaging is required to produce it. The female opening is concave and rose-shaped. It is still possible to get it wrong! Geese are best sexed at less than a week old or at six months and older; the genitals tend to look alike in between these ages. Leg ring or wing tag when sexed in order to identify later. Gentleness is vital when vent-sexing.

German Pekin ducks: An Exhibition duck, first imported by the DFT. Young ducks have a yellow hue.

Hooked Bill ducks from the Netherlands. First imported by the DFT in 1985. (Photo: Michael Roberts at The Domestic Fowl Trust.

Pomeranian geese. Imported from the U.S.A. in 1983, by the DFT, these have proved both attractive and good layers. (Photo: Michael Roberts at The Domestic Fowl Trust.

A group of White Campbell ducks. Although considered rare a few years ago, these have gained in popularity due to their utility qualities. (Photo: Michael Roberts at The Domestic Fowl Trust.

Pilgrim geese. The only true autosexing breed of goose, with the ganders pure white and the geese all grey. (Photo: Michael Roberts at The Domestic Fowl Trust.

Trout Indian Runner ducks. This is one of many colour variations. They have been described as wine bottles on stilts. (Photo: Michael Roberts at The Domestic Fowl Trust.

29

Rouen ducks at The Domestic Fowl Trust.

Toulouse geese. Originally from France, famous for pate de foie gras, made from their livers. Developed in America.

How to hold a bird for vent sexing

5. Sexing ducks and drakes

The same principal can be applied to ducks and drakes as with geese, but it is much easier to wait until they are 8-10 weeks old and listen for the quack in the female and a rasping noise in the male. Later still, the curled tail of the drake is conclusive.

6. Dual breeding

Try to avoid breeding ducks and geese together unless the ducks have an escape route through a gate or hurdle which they know about. Geese can be very territorial, particularly in the breeding season, and very savage to an unsuspecting duck out for a slug or two. They will sometimes set on them and really beat them up. This is peculiar also to young geese reared with ducklings. If the goslings become bored because of insufficient grass they will gang up and beat up a duckling. Separate rearing and breeding is best, or else have an escape route for the duck.

7. Talking to the birds

This may sound silly, but when you are working among your birds, cleaning out, fencing etc. always talk or whistle to them. The best stockmen seem to keep up a permanent monologue. The birds get to know you and are always much calmer. Ducks are particularly nervous of changes and susceptible to stress so use slow movements, try to wear the same colour clothes and don't leave anything unusual like a spade or wheelbarrow in their pen as they will spend all next day trying to avoid it. Learn to think from their point of view.

8. Age

Duck live to about 10 years of age, but their breeding effectiveness decreases after 3 years. Geese live a long time. They breed better in their second year, although most breeds will lay in their first year. The oldest goose on record (unconfirmed) in Massachusetts, USA, lived through 3 generations of one family to 101 years old. The oldest British goose on record, mentioned in The Field, was 51 years old. Average age for geese is 20-30 years. An old goose is recognised by the eye being more sunken and with more of the tear duct showing in the corner.

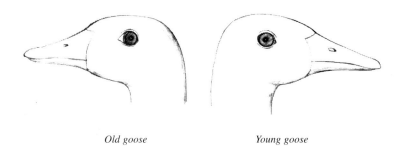

Old goose   *Young goose*

9. Plastic string

Never leave this around on the floor or use it to tie up things in the goose enclosure. Geese will undo it and try to swallow it. If you find a goose with some plastic string protruding from its beak, do not attempt to pull it out, but cut it off as close to the beak as possible and the goose should pass the rest.

10. Water

If there isn't a natural stream, pond or lake, people can be concerned about the amount of water needed for keeping ducks and geese, and dream of digging huge holes in the ground. It is always advisable to have water nearby in the form of a stand pipe or even a garden hose. Carting buckets of water is very time consuming and rather heavy work. Consider too the winter and frosts, and lag any stand pipes properly.

a) Small bowl: Ducks and geese can survive very well with a metal or plastic bowl, even a washing up bowl (green if possible), the critical point being that they must be able to get their heads into water in order to keep their eyes clean and healthy: ducks have small tear glands. These bowls must be moved around so that one area does not become muddy. One bowl per pair of ducks and two bowls per pair of geese. If you are running several breeds together always put these bowls apart as the dominant breed will tend to hog the water. They are easy to clean every day and easy to remove ice from in the winter.

b) We have developed a pond large enough for ducks and geese made of fibreglass, 198 x 92 x 15cms deep. It is easy to tip and move to fresh ground daily, and is filled by a hose attached to the ball valve fitting, ensuring a constant level. Olive green in colour, this pond has proved most successful.

c) Concrete pond: A simple and inexpensive permanent pond can be made out of concrete. The correct sitting of permanent ponds is vital. Put the pond on the driest part of the run. Note the pea gravel surround which ensures that the area around the pond where the birds spend most of their time drying off and preening is well drained and mud-free. The concrete wants to be a strong mix of 2 1/2 shovels of sand to 1 of cement and about 5 - 8cm thick. It is easy to clean every 2 days by sweeping the dirty water and debris out energetically with a hard broom. NB. DO NOT use old sunken baths or tubs. The waterfowl get in and splash about, the water level drops and they cannot get out again because of the steep and slippery sides. These tubs are also devils to keep clean.

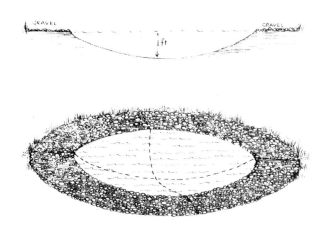

11. Grit

Good mixed grit is important for geese and ducks all year round and not just during the laying season. Place grit in a dry place in a shallow flower pot or wooden box with drainage holes. River sand is a reasonable substitute - do not use builders' sand due to the risk of setting additives contained in it.

12. Lighting

If you are keeping your duck on a strict commercial basis then getting them back to lay after the moult is all important. The moult time can be reduced from 8-12 weeks to 3 weeks by placing a low wattage bulb (20 watts) in their house to increase the daylight hours to 16. Water and food should be provided ad lib.

13. Ringing

Identification of birds is most important if you are seriously trying to improve a breed either for egg laying, growth rate, size or colour specification. There are many methods of identification including wing tags, nose bands and toe punching, but the commonest is leg-ringing, probably because the birds can be identified from a distance. Do buy and fit the bird with the right size ring otherwise it will slip off, or be too tight and cause pain and lameness, or snag on grass and roots.

a) Plastic coil type: Available in 10 sizes and about 12 colours. A permanent ring which is difficult to get on and cannot be used again on another bird.

b) Flat band type: Same range of sizes and colours as (a) easy to put on and take off, can be used again. It can sometimes be pulled off by a particularly persistent goose. A temporary ring, it can be numbered with a waterproof felt pen.

c) Adjustable aluminium numbered rings: Be sure to fit correctly, flatten the lugs properly and carefully cut off the excess aluminium strip when fitting to smaller duck. A permanent ring, one size fitting all. Slightly more expensive than (a) and (b) No colour variation.

d) Wing tags: Small metal strips which are clipped into the wing skin normally near the shoulder and on the front of the wing. One size is used for all breeds as against the 20 leg ring sizes, and a pair of pliers is needed for attaching the tag. The timing of wing tagging is flexible as the bird can be tagged at any age. The tag can be removed but cannot be used again. These tags come in five different colours, and can be numbered. Safety pin type wing tags are useful as they can be used again.

Flat band leg ring

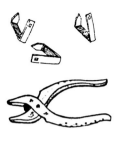

Wing tags and pliers
(see over)

14. Wing clipping and pinioning

Certain domestic duck will fly quite well and require wing clipping. These are usually the smaller and bantam varieties and also the Muscovies. If you buy these as adults, then wing clip them once a year in August. Cut the primaries on one wing only with a sharp pair of kitchen scissors as per the diagram. You are aiming to unbalance flight. There is a convenient line of smaller feathers which you use as a guide for cutting. If you cut closer to the flesh you will make the quills bleed, if you cut further away there will be enough feathers remaining to use for flight, and the procedure will therefore be ineffective.

Pinioning is a permanent way of wing clipping and should be carried out when the bird is 2-5 days old. Take the wing of the bird and with a sharp, clean pair of nail scissors cut the section as per the diagram. Your are removing the portion of the wing which contains the primaries. At this stage there is little or no blood and little stress. Best done on a cool day when flies are not so active. Pinioning is normally done automatically on ornamental waterfowl as the law states that any bird not indigenous to the UK must be pinioned at birth. It is illegal to pinion domestic waterfowl including call duck. The experienced breeder will sex the bird first and then cut, say, the right wing for male and the left wing for female. However, wing clipped domestic birds are downgraded at shows. It appears to be common practice, if wing-clipping is needed, to leave the two outer primaries uncut on show birds.

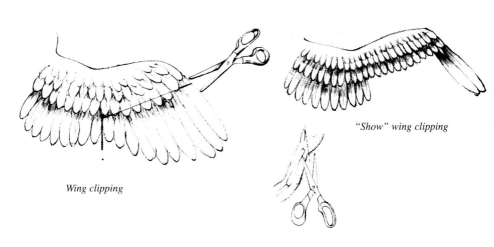

"Show" wing clipping

Wing clipping

Pinioning at day old

15. Homosexuality

This can occur in geese, particularly where there are too many ganders and not enough geese. There is not much that can be done about this once it happens as the pair bond in geese is strong. Breeding from these birds with other partners is rarely successful.

16. Imprinting

This is a survival instinct and means that a young duck or goose will consider as 'mother' the first thing it sees moving after it has hatched until it is about 24 hours old. While it can be amusing to be followed around by a little gosling it is unfair on the bird as you cannot be with it 24 hours a day and it identifies with you and not with its own species. These birds rarely breed as they do not consider themselves birds, let alone geese or duck. When ducks and geese are hatched in an incubator they form bonds between themselves and grow up as a group.

17. Transportation

If you need to transport birds they must be comfortable and safe. For ducks, strong cardboard boxes will do, particularly the type used by wine merchants. Ventilation holes are essential and are easily made by cutting 2 horizontal slits on each corner of the box near the top and then pushing in the wedge of cardboard. A layer of straw or shavings helps to soak up any liquid mess. Do not overcrowd them as the birds will sweat and can die very quickly. If you are not a handyman, tea chests with a wire mesh top are fine for geese. If you are a handyman or carpenter, a slatted crate 2'6" x 2'6" x 3' or .75 x .75 x 1 metre high makes an ideal container for a large exhibition goose or two Chinese geese. Sacks are not allowed because birds can easily suffocate inside them.

18. Disinfection of equipment

Prevention being your watchword, it is advisable to have a regular routine of disinfecting water and feed troughs. Find an old oblong water tank or something similar holding about 20 gallons, fill it with water and add Antec (Longlife 200). Soiled equipment can be left to soak and then easily cleaned with an old washing up brush and left to drain. The disinfecting solution should be changed regularly. If you stand water fonts on bricks, wash these occasionally too.

FATTENING & KILLING FOR HOME CONSUMPTION

If you intend selling birds slaughtered and prepared on your premises on a commercial basis, you must check your local Council's Environmental Health and Trading Standards to ensure that you comply with the regulations.

A) Fattening

Ducks

If you want to fatten duck it is most economical to buy some purpose-bred ducklings, advertised in Farmers' Weekly, Farmers' Guardian, Poultry World etc. as Massive Aylesburys. These are not pure bred but Pekin-Aylesbury crosses.

These ducklings may arrive in a box by road carrier, so have a place ready for them as described on page 23. Feed them ad lib with chick starter crumbs for the first two weeks to ensure they get the correct balance of proteins and vitamins. Ducks can be very nervous when young and panic easily: the moonlight shining into their house, a twig scratching the roof will send them scurrying. They are very vulnerable to rats. At three weeks they need a change in rearing system to a stable or shed with a false floor or weld mesh or wooden slats. Straw is all right, but you will have to clean this out daily. These ducks mature quicker than pure breeds. They do best confined but not overcrowded and kept away from swimming water but with access to grass if suitable. The basic idea is not to let them run off their flesh at free range.

At 2 weeks gradually introduce growers chips or small pellets with some wheat or barley. Mix this in with the chick crumbs and feed ad lib, gradually decreasing the growers chips and adding more wheat and barley. Continue until the 6th week when you can feed pure barley or wheat. Maize can be used, but it will turn the skin and fat yellow. Do not forget mixed grit.

If you feel strongly about chemicals in commercial fattening food and want to rear your birds on plain grain, do start with the chick crumbs so that the correct balance of protein, carbohydrates, fat and vitamins is maintained for the first two crucial weeks. Ducklings can be severely stunted at this age by incorrect feeding. Beware of anticoccidiosis drugs in chick crumbs, however, these have been known to be fatal to ducks. If in doubt, ask your supplier. After three weeks, gradually introduce wheat and barley and any COOKED scraps from your kitchen. The birds should be ready for killing at 10-11 weeks.

Oats seem to be ducks' least favourite food.

Excess drakes

If you find yourself with an excess of drakes at the end of the breeding season, and we usually do, you can make some useful table birds out of them, confining them away from the other birds and away from swimming water with just troughs for drinking. They should be given wheat or barley ad lib, with fattening ration if desired, in the house out of sight of sparrows and starlings. Try not to stress them, and check their weight and feathering (to ensure the moult has finished) every week. 4 weeks indoors should be enough.

Geese

The best geese are fattened naturally outside on grass with some whole wheat or barley fed to them in the morning and afternoon. Do not allow access to swimming water and allow roughly 20 geese per acre, depending on the state of the pasture. Water should be given in oblong troughs 7 - 10cm deep by 15cm wide and 1 metre long. A water system can be set up with a polythene hose and automatic drinkers if the numbers dictate. Do remember that geese have to be able to dip their heads under the water to keep their eyes clean.

If you want to run the geese on until Christmas then you must give them additional barley or wheat morning and afternoon. They are best confined one month before killing. The appetite of a goose is more regulated than a duck so ad lib feeding is merely attracting rats. Cooked household scraps can be added, and as the goodness has mostly gone out of the grass by this time, additional greenstuffs can be provided by sugar beet tops, if they are grown in your area, or trimmings from a greengrocer. Geese also love fruit. Beware of feeding maize as this gives the skin and fat a yellow colour. An oven ready fat goose weighs 3/4 of its live weight. Christmas geese should fetch up to £2.50 per lb.

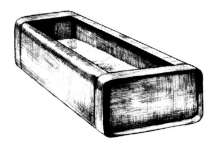

A suitable trough for ducks and geese

B) When to kill

Check that the birds have no stub or pin feathers, that these have all grown through. Normally with young stock, say Pekins, the best time is 9-12 weeks, young Muscovies 14-16 weeks. Young geese, if they are killed at the end of October are known as Green or Michaelmas geese. Some people prefer to run them on until Christmas, but it can be preferable to kill all the Christmas geese at Michaelmas because

a) they freeze very well.

b) they cost less in feeding as the weather should still be reasonably warm, but they may not be as heavy.

c) they don't have that off-putting layer of heavy yellow fat and are therefore less greasy.

C) How to kill

Deprive the birds of food for 6-8 hours or overnight before you kill them, but give them access to drinking water. Always kill the birds out of sight and hearing of the others. The method of killing we have used for years is an air gun for large waterfowl. It is instantaneous and totally effective. Hang the bird up by its feet with the head along the ground, place the muzzle of the airgun to the back of the head then pull the trigger.

If you do not possess an airgun then use the broom handle method for dislocation of the neck. Hold the bird by its feet, head down on the floor, and lay the broom handle across the neck behind the head. It will probably need two of you to do this, one of whom should be at least 6' tall. With both feet on the broom handle, thus squeezing the neck, jerk the bird's feet upwards. This requires quite a bit of strength. Tie the bird up by the feet to allow the blood to collect in the neck.

With both methods of killing there can be quite a lot of flapping after the bird is technically dead. This is the nerves still twitching and it continues for about a minute.

1. Traditional hand plucking

It is always easier to pluck birds when they are still warm. Remove the large tail and wing feathers and put them in a separate bag. If you are plucking a few birds then set a room or area aside as feathers and fluff go everywhere. (Beware, allergy sufferers). Lay plastic on the floor if you want to keep the feathers (see Feathers, page 43). Now lay the bird on the edge of a table with the head hanging over and gently start to pull the feathers out away from the direction in which they are growing. Once the bird is clear of all body feathers to half way up the neck, pick off any stubs or pin feathers with a blunt kitchen knife held to your thumb.

Singeing

This is done to remove any last bits of fluff. A small butane torch such as plumbers use is ideal, but an alternative is two tablespoons of methylated spirits set alight in an ovenproof dish. Try not to scorch the skin: it should be a swift operation. The smell is a bit unpleasant.

2. Wet plucking

Immerse the bird in a large pan or electric boiler of scalding water for a couple of minutes then hang it up by its legs to drip: wipe with an old tea towel to help dry it. Start to pluck the feathers beginning with the large and coarse ones in the wings and tail. Pluck onto a large plastic sheet if you want to use the feathers (see Feathers page 53). If the feathers do not come out easily, immerse again. Experience will teach you the optimum time for each size of bird. Pick over and singe. The skins may remain reddened by this method.

3. Dry plucking

When the bird is killed, wrap a damp towel or old nappy around it and using an old electric iron, iron over the bird for a few minutes. Hang the bird up by its feet and start to pluck, taking care not to tear the skin. If the feathers do not come out easily, iron again. Pluck the large and coarse feathers separately and use a plastic sheet on the floor. Pick over and singe.

4. Other plucking methods

There are a number of plucking machines available for the larger user and these are definitely worth investigating. The quality is variable, so try and arrange a demonstration.

Hanging

This is a matter of personal preference. It can help to tenderise the meat and improve the flavour. The birds must be hung in a totally fly proof place which should be cool and airy. A small cupboard with hooks inside and fly screen let into the doors is useful. Alternatively make a frame, cover it with cheesecloth and suspend from a beam: make sure that the birds hanging inside are at least 5cm away from the cheesecloth otherwise blowflies will still be able to lay eggs on them.

Dressing

Cut off wings at second joint. Cut the head off at the line of neck feathers: this flap of skin is used in trussing to keep the juices in. Cut the skin on the back of the neck to between the shoulder blades (a) and remove the neck with a strong pair of scissors or pruning shears (b). Then remove the windpipe, crop and gullet. With a sharp kitchen knife or scissors cut around the vent (c). Try to avoid cutting the gut. Make the hole large enough to work two fingers up to the front of the bird and in two operations, first pull out the intestines and gizzard (a hard lump about halfway up the bird) and then the heart, lungs and liver (d). The neck giblet can be used for stock and the liver for pate. Make sure the gall bladder (green) does not break as it will bitterly taint the liver. Break and twist off the legs at 12 - 25cm below the hock (elbow) (e). Wash out the bird and pat dry with kitchen paper.

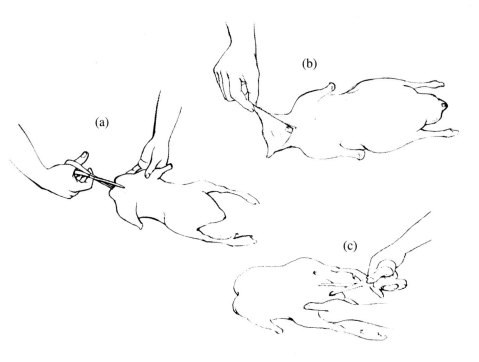

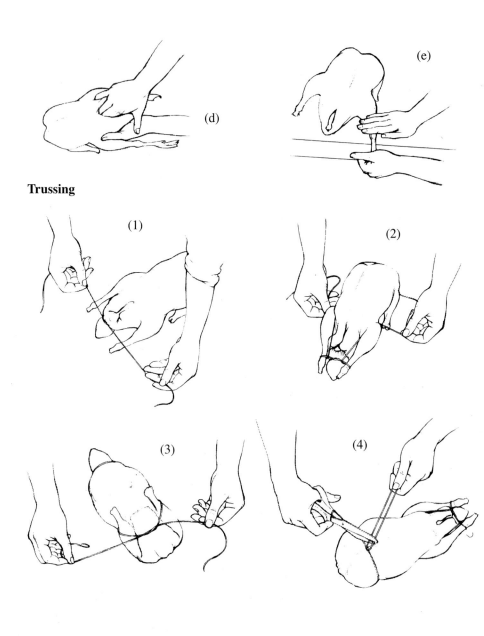

Trussing

(d)

(e)

(1)

(2)

(3)

(4)

Place in a plastic bag, remove all the air and seal with a twist tie, label with weight and date, and freeze.

Ducks and geese are best thawed slowly in the fridge overnight. With an old bird only fit for casseroling, it can save a lot of time if you just skin it without plucking.

Feathers

If you want to use the feathers for cushions, pillows or duvets then they must be sterilised. You will have plucked the finer feathers onto a plastic sheet or into a box and not mixed in the coarse or badly soiled ones.

A good method of sterilising the feathers and down, is to bake them in a slow oven. Washing affects the insulation properties of the feathers and does not sterilise them. Either sew them into an old pillowcase or press them down into a casserole pan with a lid, the biggest that will fit into your oven. Use an electric oven at 180 degrees F or the slow oven of an Aga for 2 hours. Do not use high heat as the feathers will merely burn.

When cool, the feathers can be stored in bin bags until you are ready to use them or sell them. In order to make pillows, cushions or duvets it is essential to use a material called ticking, which has a very close weave, to contain the feathers. Use any other material and you will get feathers poking through - very scratchy. Sew the ticking together in the desired pattern, turn right side out leaving a gap for stuffing - wide enough to get a big handful of feathers into easily. Do not overstuff.

One goose will yield 5-6oz usable feathers.

Mallard coloured Call Drake: yield of feathers approximately 1 oz.

VERMIN CONTROL

Fox proof fence

Three styles of fox proof fencing

1. 2.44m wooden posts with 1.83m x 5cm mesh wire netting and electric wire near base, another near the top.

3. 2.44m or 2.75m wooden posts with 92cm by 5cm mesh on top then 1.22m x 5cm mesh down to meet 1.22m x 25mm on ground and on the side.

2. 5cm x 5cm angle iron with 1.83cm x 5cm mesh on overhang and down to meet 1.22m x 25mm mesh on ground and up the side.

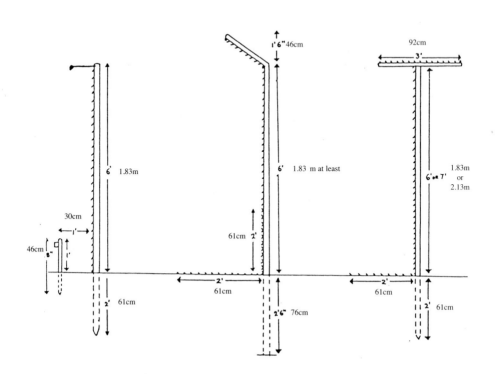

VERMIN CONTROL

Foxes

Foxes are a menace to waterfowl and will kill indiscriminately. A fox will normally check to see if you have closed your birds in for the night - so many times have we heard "The one night I forgot to shut in the birds, the fox got them". When checking, they follow a set route every time, scenting as they go. Sometimes you can smell them in the morning where they have scented. The best solution is to prevent them from entering the entire area and this means you need less housing. See "Modern Vermin Control" book for more details (back cover).

Winged vermin

These include magpies, rooks, crows and jays. Winged vermin will take eggs and youngsters and leave no visible signs. Encourage your birds to lay under cover, and collect the eggs early in the morning. Put netting over runs where young are kept. Shooting winged vermin requires getting up before daybreak and sitting in a hen house or shed near to where you suspect eggs or young are being taken. Use crow decoys if you have them - these are particularly effective if used with a device which rests the decoy on a branch or wire so that it moves with any breeze. Let your birds out if they are fenced in and place a few eggs in full view. Your patience should be rewarded - do not give the vermin the chance to fly away.

I once had a rogue crow which was taking 3 week old ducklings. I had thought at the time it was a stoat as the thefts were regular, the birds being attacked on the back of the neck - typical stoat activity. I was waiting with gun poised expecting to see a bitch stoat, obviously feeding her young, when suddenly a large carrion crow landed on the ground, chose its meal and jumped onto the back of a squealing duck. The shot I took was lucky - as I fired, the duck with the crow on its back disappeared behind a metal water font: I killed the crow, peppered the font and the duck survived the day.

Magpies and crows can be trapped successfully in a live-catch trap with a decoy. The Larsen Trap works on the territory principle: resident birds will try to drive out a stranger. It is approved by the RSPB, and should you catch any non-target species it is easy to release them.

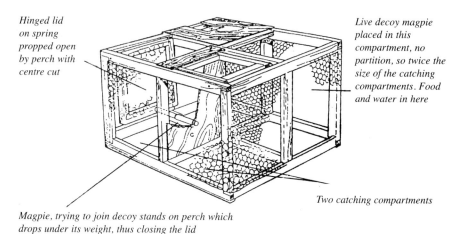

Two catching compartments

*Magpie, trying to join decoy stands on perch which
drops under its weight, thus closing the lid*

Larsen Trap

Rats, Stoats and Weasels

Rats are always a problem. They spread disease and eat eggs and youngsters. Try to prevent any excess food from lying around, and construct housing which is not suitable for rats to burrow under i.e. raised at least 23cm off the ground. It is well to have some traps permanently set, see diagram. Stoats and weasels will eat eggs and youngsters and are best caught by trapping. The trap must be set in a tunnel (or DFT Rat box) to prevent any other species from being caught, and must be checked at least once every day.

Set Fenn Trap

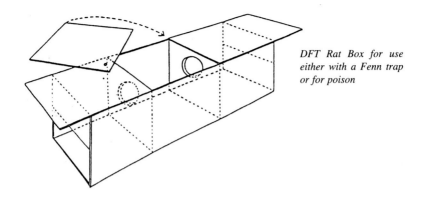

DFT Rat Box for use either with a Fenn trap or for poison

To wipe out a colony that is well established, find all the rat holes and fill all but one with a turf, well stamped in. Light a stick of Murphy's Mole Ban in the remaining hole then fill it in firmly. Next day, check to see if any of the holes have been opened up and if so, repeat. As the smoke is toxic, keep livestock away from the area, fencing it off if necessary.

Local Council Rodent Control Operatives are always very helpful, but the only method they use is poisoning, which may not be appropriate among the birds. (If a pet eats poison based on anticoagulants, the antidote is Vitamin K, administered by your vet. The early symptoms are lethargy and nosebleed).

Mink

Mink are vicious killers and are particularly fond of duck. They are only common in certain areas of the UK, but are spreading. Mink travel along waterways and are fairly easily caught in cage traps baited with kipper. These traps should be set on established runs or paths. If a water vole is caught instead, it can be released unharmed. The correct way to dispatch a mink caught in your trap is to shoot it. The scent of the first caught mink will attract others to the trap.

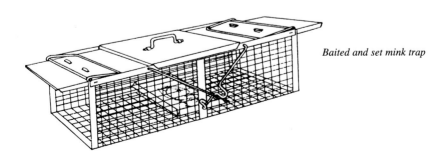

Baited and set mink trap

EXHIBITING

One of the most essential parts of breeding quality stock is exhibiting at shows. Showing and breeding go hand in hand. Anyone can keep inferior stock and the cost of keeping is the same as for good stock.

If you want to show your birds, go first to one of the waterfowl shows organised by the BWA or any of the large shows with a waterfowl section. Talk to the breeders there and try to learn something of the art of showing and what the judges are looking for - see the BWA Standards book. Fortunately with ducks and geese there is little faking, perhaps the odd miscoloured feather being pulled out.

Having seen the show birds, are your birds up to that size and quality? The quickest way to get into showing is by buying top exhibition stock, and in some cases you will have to pay dearly. Find out who consistently wins or is in the top four in that particular breed and introduce yourself at one of the shows. Most top breeders are very affable and only too delighted to encourage beginners. They may offer you stock for sale, but you must remember that they will be offering you their second best birds. This is where experience helps. The breeder is unlikely to sell you any of his prize-winning stock, and you cannot tell which they are anyway (see Permanent Identification page 50). Try to buy as near as possible in quality to his best stock and you should be given a choice of birds. Often there may be quite visible faults or deformities (check the Standards) so these can be ruled out straight away: sometimes a bird has had an accident; it may be missing a toenail or have torn the web of its foot. This bird will be passed over for showing but could be a good stock bird to breed from in the future.

Assuming you have selected your birds for showing, find out when and where the shows are, who is the secretary dealing with the waterfowl entries and when the entries close. This is always at least one month before the show and sometimes more. Entries cost from £1.00 to £2.50 each at the larger shows. Fancy Fowl publishes a useful list of forthcoming shows and results of others.

Try entering as many birds as you can: it will speed up your learning as to why certain birds win while others do not, and help you to get over the feelings of disappointment when prizes don't appear.

As with any type of showing, personality clashes can occur. It is difficult to be aloof from these petty differences: the main thing is to note the warring factions and concentrate on the birds.

Preparing for the show

You will need to bring your birds in from free range about a week before the show. To get them used to the idea of the show cage, construct similar ones and pen them separately. Keep the cages together so they can at least hear the others. Bring in more birds than you expect to show. This way you can pick the best.

The cage sizes for   bantam/Call ducks are 38cm x 38cm x 38cm

standard ducks are 46cm x 46cm x 46cm

geese are 61cm x 61cm x 61cm

It is no good trying to show a bird that cowers in the furthest corner of its cage or snaps and hisses in fear at the judges. Keep the cages if you can in a busy place so the birds get used to the idea of people around them, being handled, fed and watered, and they will quickly lose their fear. The idea is to get the bird to feel comfortable in the cage and that way it will show itself to the best advantage.

Feeding is important as these birds are under stress. A few extra goodies are needed and ad lib water into which they can get their heads. It is vital to keep them clean, particularly if you are showing white birds, as their feathers will stain. Maize which contains a yellow pigment called xyanthophyl can help to improve the beak and leg colour in white ducks, such as Pekins, White Campbells and White Call ducks, but use with caution as it is a very heating and fattening food.

Before putting the birds into their show containers, you may need to wash them, particularly underneath, and their feet and legs. Use warm water and a soft nail brush. Allow them to dry on some clean straw or shavings. A lot of preening and rubbing of the oil gland will go on as they dry. Inspect the feet, legs and bill very carefully and ensure the eyes and nostrils are clean. Gently rub some Vaseline on the beak and legs - it brings out the colour well. Your bird is now ready to be boxed.

You will need to transport your birds particularly carefully for showing. At the shows you will see all sorts of containers, from Hessian lined baskets and custom made varnished wooden boxes with the breeder's name printed on the side through to cardboard cartons and tea chests. You can buy boxes and baskets at some of the major shows; the idea is for your bird to arrive comfortable, cool and clean.

Don't be tempted to exhibit sick or poorly feathered birds just becaue you have paid an entry fee. It helps neither the show nor the birds, nor, for that matter, your future reputation as a breeder of quality stock.

Showing is stressful to your birds, so keep an eye on them once you get home again to make sure they have recovered properly. A little pampering does no harm.

On the day of the show, do not overfeed your ducks and geese in the morning before judging. A bulging crop can ruin the otherwise elegant lines of a bird, but improves breeds with a heavy keel.

Show breeding

It is impossible to go into all aspects of breeding for showing as each breed has its own conditions. You have to remember that all breeds of domestic waterfowl are man-made and will continue to be influenced by him. Therefore there are ways of improving each breed by selection, feeding, time of breeding etc., knowledge of which is mostly gained by experience. Standards do change from time to time.

Permanent identification

All other domestic stock kept by man is subject to very careful recording, from cattle, sheep, pigs, through to dogs, cats and rabbits; also pigeons, budgerigars and canaries but why not poultry?

There is no official record of breeding lines of ducks and geese in the UK, nothing to tell you which bird has won, no history or stud books. We know that there are a few reputable breeders who do keep their own records, but there is the continuing problem of access to them - what happens to these records and birds after that person dies? It was the same with Mendel - ignorant people destroying valuable works.

We believe it is necessary for the conservation and study of domestic fowl to have properly recorded bloodlines and genetic information. The only way this can be achieved is by permanently and accurately identifying the birds and by only accepting birds for showing which are accurately identified.

DISEASES AND AILMENTS

Of all the domestic fowl, geese and ducks suffer the least from diseases. Most of their ailments are caused through bad management such as lack of, or dirty water, overcrowding or wet bedding. Virkon by Antec is a disinfectant effective against all poultry pathogens.

1. Aspergillosis

A respiratory disease caused by a fungus present in mouldy hay, mouldy food and damp bedding. Never use hay - straw and shavings are best. Particularly seen under artificial rearing conditions, rarely when the birds are reared naturally. Symptoms are gasping, breathing hard and rapidly, and general weakness. Weaker birds will die, some will recover, especially if the source of the fungus is removed. Move affected birds to new quarters and disinfect affected area with Virkon.

2. Pneumonia

Easily contracted by goslings when they are turned out too soon and get caught in a heavy shower. They have very little protection from the elements as they feather from the underneath first. A chill will quickly turn to pneumonia unless the birds are brought into a warm place: if very cold almost lifeless, put under an infra red lamp with Terramycin in the drinking water and chick crumbs available. Keep indoors until fully recovered. Early symptoms are a drunken gait and heavy breathing. Is also seen in youngsters reared on damp and filthy bedding.

3. Worms

Ducks and geese of all ages are susceptible to worms, particularly gizzard worms which burrow into the gizzard, also gape worms which live in the windpipe. Stale ground can contribute to the worm burden, so it is advisable to worm at least once a year with Flubenvet in the feed, but not during the breeding season. Add this white powder to the food, mix and feed in a trough or plastic basin. Symptoms are sudden lameness, loss of weight and general lethargy and lack of egg production.

4. Stress

Stressed birds will succumb to any small amount of bacteria or viruses present in their bodies; stress lowers the bird's natural resistance. Management and care must be improved during stress so that the birds can recover as quickly as possible. Heavier birds, particularly duck, can go off their legs if they get too hot from travelling or are chased around in order to be caught. Recovery time is from a few minutes to a few days. Add protexin to drinking water.

5. Angel wings

This is where the last joint of the wing from where the primaries grow, twists, resulting in that portion of the wing sticking out from the body at an unnatural angle. It can affect one or both wings on a bird, and is seen in wild and domestic geese. The cause is feeding too high a level of protein to growing goslings and ducklings, between the ages of 6 weeks and 20 weeks. There is a build up of amino acids in the quills of the flight or primary feathers, which adds weight to that section of the wing and causes it to droop. It can first be detected when you notice the birds consistently trying to hitch up their wings. The rearing food needs to be changed immediately with proteins down to 12%. The wings can be saved with the use of masking tape, but this isn't a 100% cure.

6. Corns

Corns appear if birds don't have access to swimming water and are kept on tough, spiky grass or rough ground. They can appear in either winter or summer and will make the birds lame. Give the bird access to swimming water and the corns should heal themselves. Sometimes the webs will crack and tear.

7. Sore eyes

Caused by dirty water and the bird being unable to immerse its head in water to clean its eyes. Also seen in winter when it is cold with ice on the water and chapping winds. Wash gently with tepid water around the eye and gently apply a mild healing ointment on the worst chapped areas. Golden Eye ointment works well.

8. Sunstroke or July staggers

This is caused by lack of food and water in strong sunshine. The symptoms are a staggering gait in the early stages followed by going off the legs, and the head and neck weaving uncontrollably. Immediate action is vital as the bird's temperature rises dramatically which can lead to brain damage. Put the bird in a cool place on an old sack or something similar. Cover its body with a sack and prop up its head with another like a collar to stop its head weaving. A Roslamb feeder is invaluable here as it makes getting water into the bird relatively easy. The Roslamb feeder consists of a plastic, calibrated cylinder connected to a long thin tube with special holes so that liquid goes down easily. Push the tube down the bird's throat - it will automatically swallow it so you need not fear damaging or drowning the bird - and give it 30ml of clean, tepid water every 10 minutes for 1/2 an hour, propping up the head so the water does not come out again. Continue giving the tepid water every 1/2 hour for a further two hours. Leave the bird covered and propped up overnight but not with a heat lamp, and in the morning it should be on its feet. Give food and water ad lib until it is fully recovered, and then return it to its pen outside.

9. Prolapse

This is most often seen in good laying ducks, but can occur in drakes and also in geese. There will be a red protruberance at the vent with maybe 5cm of organs sticking out. Once a prolapse has occurred the bird should be culled.

10. Accidental deaths

Any small piece of wire can be picked up by ducks and geese as they are very curious, and geese particularly like playing with things: a piece of wire, if swallowed will normally be ground up in the gizzard - even glass has been found smooth and polished! - but if it passes through the gizzard it will perforate the intestine and the bird will die of spetacaemia. The symptoms are a bright green, pungent smelling mess. Try and find a vet who specialises in poultry (not easy) as it all adds to experience and information. Gloucester Laboratories run a post mortem service. Record anything unusual and how you dealt with it in your diary.

11. Fleas and Mites

Waterfowl do not normally suffer from fleas but they can sometimes pick up mites from wild birds or from infected birds which are in shows. Spraying with Johnson's Kill Pest will control these.

12. Duck Virus Enteritis

This disease is a killer, and is seen in both young and adult birds. It is mainly caused by stale drinking water and swimming water and is sometimes carried by visiting wild mallard. The ducks die very suddenly, looking a little listless in the last 24 hours. Move to fresh ground, clean all drinking troughs, ponds etc. with Virkon S and allow drinking water only with Terramycin added for a week.

USEFUL ADDRESSES AND SUPPLIERS

British Waterfowl Association, c/o Mrs R. Boer, Oaklands, Blind Lane,
Tanworth in Arden, Solihull, B94 5HS. Tel: 01564 741821

An association of enthusiasts, membership, tri-annual magazine, Breeders' Directory.

British Goose Producers Association, High Holborn House, 52-54 High Holborn,
London WC1V 6SX

Commercial goose production

Gloucester Laboratories (Veterinary) Ltd., St. Oswolds Road, Cattlemarket,
Gloucester GL1 2SL

Post Mortem Service.

INDEX

NOTES

NOTES